Alzheim...

My Turn Next?

By Jemima Atkinson

John Atkinson (1921–2007)

Copyright Jemima Atkinson 2018

First published in 2018

By Milton Contact Ltd

A CIP catalogue record for this book is available from

The British Library

ISBN: 978-1-911526-20-9

Printed in United Kingdom

Milton Contact Ltd

3 Hall End, Milton, Cambridge. UK

CB24 6AQ

Cover: Lillie Langtry, painting by Edward Poynter, Courtesy of the Jersey Heritage Collections

2

Contents

Introduction

I am writing about my own experience with caring for people with dementia because it is in my family big time. In fact, I was expecting to succumb to it first.

We need to find a cure or at least help prevent dementia, it is such a horrible disease. Not only does the sufferer become a different person, but it is very isolating and quite frightening for friends and relatives alike. You never know what to say or do. There isn't a manual for coping because we are all different and it is the personality that is destroyed as well as the finances which makes it very hard on families struggling to cope.

I have given talks about my experience at meetings. What follows is my story of caring for a loved one, my husband John Atkinson, with dementia. I hope that by sharing it, it will help you if you are in a similar situation. You are not alone.

How it all started

We lived in Brookside in a Victorian terraced house on five floors, overlooking the Leys School in Cambridge. Hobson's Brook separated us from the main road, where all manner of water fowl swam up and down, much to the delight of tourists and visiting friends of our children and grandchildren.

This particular Friday afternoon, John had invited a young lady to tea whom I had never met, who was supposedly a financial Whiz Kid in London. She arrived at the back door, having parked her car in the lane behind the house at the same time as the young man who had been restoring the portrait of my great-grandfather arrived at the front door.

Naturally we introduced them to each other and tea was served, as were the biscuits.

John loved biscuits! Conversation flowed as did the tea until John disappeared to go to the loo. He seemed to be gone a long time and came back shivering, shaking and talking complete rubbish.

Nicola, the young lady, got off her chair and started to put on her coat saying, "Is that really the time? I

6

ought to be getting home." Whereupon John gave her his house keys to start her car! Giles, the young man, got off his step-ladder, having just hung great-grandfather, and said something about the bill and disappeared.

After they had gone I made John a hot water bottle and put him to bed where he slept for hours and hours and woke up a completely different person.

Things gradually deteriorated. First it was just constant repetition, and then other things started to happen. Milk would be put back in the cupboard instead of the fridge. Just little things like that to begin with and then they escalated.

The basement was then cleared of stuff, and the builders moved in. My plan was for it to be a self-contained flat, so that John could live there with a carer, if and when the time came! John would not leave the builders alone. He was up and down the stairs all day, unless I took him out of the house. They were very good about it. But as soon as it was finished, which took approximately 6 months, he refused to go down the stairs again!

John Atkinson: Navigator, Prisoner of War, Actor, Writer, Husband & Father

8

John's life before Alzheimer's

John was always a dreamer. His school report read "Would do better if he were with us more often!", and this was boarding school! He achieved unexpectedly good results, but it wasn't long before the start of WWII.

John had wanted to go in to the Navy, but he had red-green colour blindness, as does Jonathan his 9 year old grandson whom he never met, so he volunteered to train as a Navigator in a Lancaster bomber. Soon he was part of a 6-man team in a Lancaster bomber, navigating the others over various sites in Germany.

The pilot was an Australian and they went everywhere together. John told me that he and Keith Barnes, the pilot, called all the other members of the crew "tail end Charlies" as you never got to know them personally.

He would regale us with tales of many scrapes during this time! One I remember was John and Keith running late after being held up on an exercise in a small plane. They were worried that they would be too late to take out a couple of girls for the evening when they discovered there was a queue at the landing strip.

So, they radioed to the airfield "Flying on one engine only, flying on one engine only, request permission to land". Assuming it to be an emergency in a standard four-engine plane, they were bumped up the queue and able to scurry home in time! Only once they had landed safely, did air traffic control and their commanding officer discover that it was only a single engine aircraft! Needless to say their CO was not amused and gave them a piece of his mind.

John told me that if shot down he was sure that he would go down with the plane but much to his astonishment, when they "bought it" on their last mission in January 1944, he found himself hanging from a tree trapped in his parachute. Keith had literally pushed hum out of the plane after it was hit and, with the others, he was assumed Missing in Action and awarded the DFC.

He was in fact found by a German farmer who told him off for bombing innocent women and children, instead of staying at home with his mother, before taking him to hospital. From there, he was transferred to a variety of prisoner of war camps until the end of the war.

John spent the last 6 months of the war on "Death Marches" from camp to camp. The Germans knew of the approaching Allies so they kept them permanently on the move. John did not speak German so decided his role was to entertain his fellow prisoners. So good did he become that he decided that if he survived to the end of the war he would become an actor. This he did. He performed with the Royal Shakespeare Company and the National Theatre, as well as some television shows including Emmerdale Farm.

This was when he came in to my life on a boat in "little Venice" on Regents Park Canal, to which we were both invited to 21st birthday celebration. I through the birthday girl and he through her boyfriend!!

A few years later following a few minor roles in films and television he played the Butler in Oscar Wilde's "An Ideal Husband with Michael Denison and Dulcie Gray at the Strand Theatre. It was during this time that we were married. The newspapers had a field day as you can imagine. "Mary Malcolm's daughter marries her "Ideal Husband".

The Australian Connection

Years later again, after we had moved into Cambridge for the education of our 3 daughters, we received a phone call from a girl we had never met with an Australian accent. Her name was Trish Barnes.

She told me that her Uncle Keith was the pilot of the plane that came down over Berlin and that all the men in her family were pilots and all the women nurses.

Trish herself had won an award to study Breast Cancer at the Royal Marsden Hospital in London and could she come and see us – which she duly did and became like another daughter for us. While she was here her older brother Ric flew for Qantas and used to come and stay in Cambridge when he had a stopover in London.

How strange is that? We were invited to Ric's wedding, but John declined the invitation. However Trish and Bob (her father) came to Tessa and Liam's wedding and I went to both Ric's sister's weddings – one in Australia and one in Canada. Tessa, Liam and Natalie came with me to the wedding in Canada.

Childhood Memories - Tessa

Dad wasn't keen on talking about his war time experience, but we did a project on it at primary school and so dragged some information out of him. He told us that all those "pests" who would try and escape used the bed boards to shore up the tunnels. Now this worked when they were only there for long enough for them to leave 3 boards – 1 at the head 1 at the feet and 1 in the middle. It became more of a problem however if they took the 1 in the middle without telling the person on the top bunk, as he would jump into bed as usual only to land on the poor soul beneath!

He also said that when on the marches the Red Cross parcels were wonderful as it meant they had things they could swap with the people on the road side who they realised were as hungry and cold as they were.

I remember loving "Little Red Riding Hood" so much that it drove Dad crazy, so he would call it Little Red Hooding Ride just to annoy me and I would say Riding Hood! The house in East Sheen had a long hallway upstairs and Dad would pretend to be the Big Bad Wolf from the story and he would be at one end of the hallway with Mum at the other and I would always run to Dad for protection even though technically he was the big bad wolf!

At Upwick, when I went to talk to Dad in his study he would sometimes tell me stories about 2 horses called Peaches and Cream. I used to ask him to write them down, but he never did. All I can remember now is that they pulled a milk float and were incredibly naughty.

I will also never forget the first time the hunt came on to our land and Dad went out to remonstrate with the Master of the Hunt (wearing his favourite dressing gown which only just covered enough to be decent). It did the trick as the following week we had a note through the door telling us when the hunt was coming so we could keep all the animals (cats, dogs, goats, geese and chickens) inside.

Dad told us all the time that Yorkshire was freezing and that we would never want to go there. Then one year we got the opportunity to join him on the film set of "Emmerdale Farm" as it was then. It was the most glorious summer ever, so as kids we spent our time running in out of the streams on the moors and the only reason you couldn't go on

Ilkley Moor bar tat was because you were likely to get sun stroke.

My friend Rachel told me that she was watching a Hammer House of Horror film which was incredibly scary. Then Dad came on the screen and the whole film seemed a lot less scary as "Tessa's Dad" was there.

John and Jemima Atkinson after their wedding

Living with John and Dementia

Sometimes I would lie on the bed beside John while he was asleep and stroke his hair and wonder where he was. What happened to the man I married all those years ago? Where was he now? Did that funny old man even know who he was let alone who I was?

I often wondered if it was like being in a foreign country not knowing the people, their customs or the language because everything that seemed so normal and obvious to the rest of us clearly was not so for him. His mind simply could not cope with ordinary everyday things. Yet somehow, he was certainly calm and less agitated at home than when we were out.

John never lost his ability for "putting on a show" – part of the reason the GP found it so hard to believe there was anything wrong with him – and he would entertain the grandchildren by pulling the best faces while refusing to do whatever we had asked! Working in theatre gave him excellent diction and an impressive ability to project his voice – so everyone knew exactly what he thought once all his inhibitions had gone as the Alzheimer's progressed!

It must be very strange not to be able to do the little things that everyone does without even thinking about them. I never thought that my big, strong reliable husband would become like a small helpless baby. How does this happen? How can God allow it to happen? How am I supposed to cope? What am I supposed to do? When he soiled himself, as he did frequently, I could not clean him up forever by myself, but, should I wait for someone else to come and help? How do people manage who are unable to pay for help or who are the same age? I tried to imagine.

I was lucky in that I was a lot younger than John. My friends used to tease us saying that I had married my father. In many ways, they were right. He was very much like my father and they got along very well. Except when it came to money. My father had no concept of money whatsoever which is why he never had any! Whereas John as a Yorkshireman knew only too well the value of money! He would have been horrified at how expensive part-time care at home was!

I watched John struggle with understanding ordinary everyday objects. The kind of things you and I take for granted. He would pick up a knife, and find even a cup of tea and question what it was, with his favourite phrase "Is this anything?" So much so, that it has now become a family saying! Thomasina and I often pick things up in the house and ask each other "Is this anything?" and giggle, as do her children.

It must be horrible never to know exactly who and what you are or what you are meant to be doing. The brain works in such strange ways. Yet sometimes a light would come on and he would be himself again. If only for a few minutes.

Thomasina, my eldest daughter and I used to laugh about it. One minute he would be fighting her 2 year-old son Jeremy over the counters used in the game of Connect 4 and the next he would come out with a normal adult response to a small child and we would both jump.

Now I know that this is perfectly normal and that you never entirely lose the person you love, but it is very hard to live with. Perhaps that was why I was so tired all the time. I was constantly on my guard in case I said or did something I shouldn't and made the situation worse unintentionally. But it did touch me and I now have much more empathy with people coping with difficult situations than I did before – unless it is part of the aging process.

Looking after someone with dementia isn't hard, it's just exhausting. The endless questions. The constant repetition. It just wears you out.

For me, it was like looking after a 6'2" toddler. They don't know how to behave, or their own strength, and they cannot be left on their own for a second. However, unlike toddlers, they do not gradually become civilised people, they simply become progressively less able.

John was not rude or obstreperous, he was just obstinate and very strong. Jeremy, who was 2 at the time, could be equally difficult but, as Thomasina said, the big difference was that you could pick him up and strap him into the push chair if he was having a tantrum and take him outside to "changer les idées" as the French put it. Since John was 6'2" and very strong, that was not an option!

We all got very good at distraction therapy before it was too late. He loved playing dominoes. He would re-arrange them all the time. Thomasina found him a set of plastic white ones in Tesco's and he would spend hours making them into patterns.

Lillie Langtry, Jemima's great-grandmother. By Edward Poynter, Courtesy of the Jersey Heritage Collections.

Alzheimer's is in my family

My grandmother had Alzheimer's in the 1950s but in those days, there wasn't a diagnosis as such; she was just labelled "Bonkers". From what we can gather about her mother – and my great grandmother – Lillie Langtry, it would seem that she also developed dementia in Monaco, where she died. Apparently, every night she laid a place at the dinner table for 'Darling Oscar', meaning Oscar Wilde who had been dead for years. By then, she was an old lady living on her own with a maid in Monaco.

I knew my grandmother, Lillie Langtry's daughter, as Granjan. To a child she appeared fierce and unfriendly. She would call me "child" and order me about as though I were a servant. At the same time, she was brilliant at taking us around London. She knew all the Beefeaters at the Tower of London. They all thought she was wonderful. "Yes, Lady Malcolm. No Lady Malcolm." Unknown to me, I probably saw all sorts of things that other people missed.

It was the same at the Royal Academy and Madam Tussauds. In fact, everywhere that the children could go. I shocked her aged about 8 because I loved going in the dungeons at Madame Tussauds. There was a machine there, and if you put a coin in the box you could watch Mary Queen of Scots having her head chopped off. This fascinated me so much that I spent most of my pocket money on that machine.

So, you can imagine how hard it was for me as a teenager to cope with a grandmother who was losing the plot as they say. My mother would want me to go and see her, but I never knew how she would react when I arrived. Sometimes she did not really know who I was or why I was there.

Eventually, Mummy sewed a label with her name and address printed on it to her coat. She was often picked up by the police because she wandered around Knightsbridge scantily dressed.

When she got too bad, she was labelled 'Bonkers' and shut up in St Andrews Hospital in Northampton. Just another bedbound old lady in a ward full of bedbound old ladies. Her son Angus and I were the last family members to see her alive.

I remember driving there with Uncle Angus in the 1950s. The grounds were beautiful and we went up the stairs into this enormous room full of old ladies. The room opened into a balcony. There were beds all along the balcony which was bathed in sunshine. Neither of us knew which one she was. We had to ask one of the nurses. She immediately went to fetch GranJan's grey curls and glasses.

I had never seen her without them before. She hardly acknowledged our presence but her face lit up when she spotted a young French woman and immediately attracted her attention and spoke to her in French. Uncle Angus and I looked at each other in astonishment. This was the language of her youth as she was brought up in Paris until the age of 7 by her mother Lillie Langtry's family. We stayed and talked with her for a little while in a language we used to call 'franglais.' Granjan loved it. Little did I know that she would die shortly after we left.

Mary Malcolm, Jemima's Mother, Live BBC Radio and TV Announcer

Mother and Colin

At the same time as John was starting his struggles with Alzheimer's in Cambridge, my mother's own battle with Alzheimer's was progressing fast in London. When we were children she was working for the BBC as Mary Malcolm. one of the first TV presenters. However, by this stage she had been married to my step-father Colin for over 50 years.

It was hard at the beginning to convince Colin that there was anything wrong with my mother. He saw her as an exotic plant or beautiful live ornament. Mellie, my step-sister, had joined an agency in London similar to the one I was using in Cambridge except that Mum, with her Alzheimer's progressing, now needed 24-hour care, so they converted part of the house into a flat and had live-in carers.

Colin, was paying the bills but was clearly not capable of looking after Mum himself. Apart from anything else, he was in denial about her dementia, which is apparently quite normal! My role was to go up to London once a month and take him to the Royal Free Hospital for his lung cancer appointment.

They were continuing to come to lunch with John and me once a week. The last time they came, Mum wanted to go to the loo but had no idea what to do. I literally had to take her like a toddler, pull down her pants, while she protested and did her best to stop me by pulling my clothes and scratching my arms. Meanwhile, Colin and John were attempting to talk to each other about the garden! It was like something between a nightmare and a Hitchcock film!

Apparently, it had taken until 12:20 to get Mum dressed and we could all see that this had to end, although I could see that we provided respite for Colin.

That was the last time that they were able to visit us. Mum continued to live at home until Colin passed away.

The progression of John's dementia

Getting a diagnosis

This was very difficult to get as John was very clever at disguising what was going on. Our family doctor, Hugh, looked at me over the top of his glasses and obviously did not see that we had a problem. In fact, he gave the impression of thinking "There is nothing wrong with him, whatever is the matter with her?" – which was most frustrating!

One of my church friends suggested I contact the local Alzheimer's Society. That is when Barry Plumpton came into my life. I clearly remember telling him that I did not need him! Very sensibly, he agreed, but also said that I soon would and at least would know what he looked like! He told me to ask for an assessment. I had no idea what that meant, but next time we visited Hugh I asked the vital question. He still looked at me over the top of his glasses, but this time he obviously listened as the next day the phone rang and I was told the psychiatrist was on her way.

The knife

The psychiatrist's words kept ringing in my ears, "Let him do what he can do." Unfortunately, I never quite knew what that meant. Some days he appeared almost normal, and others totally confused.

One morning in March 2004 I asked him to set the table for lunch. He gave me a very strange look and went to the drawer to get out the knives and forks. I still do not know what happened next. All I can remember saying is, "John, we do not need all those forks. No-one is coming. There are only two of us here." Whereupon he picked up a butter knife and threw it at me, walked out of the room, slammed the door and shouted, "Do it yourself!"

This was completely out of character even for the new version of John. I stood at the kitchen sink where I was washing up, sobbing. "What did I do wrong? No, he hadn't wanted to hurt me, but…"

A friend came to sit with him later that evening while I went to a concert. I told her what had happened and made an attempt to laugh it off, saying it was so unlike him I am sure it will never happen again. She said, "Everyone says that the first time it happens. You must tell the CPN." (Community Psychiatric Nurse). So I did and the next thing I knew, the psychiatrist had arranged for him to be admitted to the Denbigh Ward at Addenbrooke's Hospital in Cambridge and would I take him in at 8:30 that night.

I put the phone down and sat in a state of shock. I knew nothing about the Denbigh. No-one had warned me that this might happen, and the worst part was that the CPN made it sound as though I was very lucky to get a place at such short notice. How I got there, I will never know. John stuck by my side like a naughty child, as I packed a few toiletries in a bag and put him in the car and we duly set off. How they were going to cope with his deafness I had no idea – but I felt instinctively that it was no longer my problem.

How fast my little world was changing. We had been married 38 years. The anniversary was due in April, while he was there. In that time, we had produced 3 daughters, the youngest of whom had died in 1994 of carbon monoxide poisoning. We had seen her through 10 years of anorexia nervosa before that. The other two were both married and had babies – both girls.

In all that time, John had never raised his voice in anger to any of us. He was known as a 'gentle giant'. I was the one who had mood swings. Now, suddenly, our whole life together had been turned on its head.

Assessment on the Denbigh Ward

The senior nurse at the Denbigh called me into his office while someone else took John away. It felt as though I was voluntarily condemning him to life in a prison without even a fair trial. I felt completely helpless and empty.

The senior nurse explained that he would be kept in for a minimum of 3 weeks for an 'assessment' and that I was not to come and visit him for at least a week. At this I burst into tears and rang everyone including Thomasina, my eldest daughter who was a lawyer.

She suggested I ring PAS, the Patient Advisory Service at Addenbrooke's. They did not sound very helpful but offered to contact the Denbigh on my behalf. Suddenly the Denbigh sprung into action. I was allowed to see John. He was pacing up and down like a caged lion. I was frightened, as I had not seen him like this before. It was our wedding anniversary while he was there, so they arranged for us to have the meal on our own away from the other residents.

I seem to remember one of the staff saying to him, "Please hold it together John for your wife's sake while she is here," which seemed to me to be a very strange thing to say. Later I discovered that he had threatened to throttle the staff and jump out of the window.

The girls, Thomasina and Tessa, turned up with their baby daughters much to the delight of the other residents. They brought toys and games with them in theory to keep the children amused, but the residents enjoyed them as much as the little ones as there was no visible sign of anything for the residents to do. All they did was walk around and around the building and go out into a small courtyard.

After 3 weeks, the psychiatrist rang and asked me to go to his office at the Denbigh. It would seem that John was so aggressive that they were unable to do an *assessment* (whatever that meant), so I was to take him home.

Getting help at home

Private untrained carers

Once he came out of the Denbigh Ward, both Thomasina and Tessa were horrified at the idea that John would just come straight home to me. "Mummy, Dad hates you for taking him there. You can't be on your own with him, he will kill you." So, remembering that my step-sister had employed someone from Christies, a South African agency, to care for my step-father, I rang them and explained the problem. "Bridget," they said, "might be free to come". They did not promise anything as it was very short notice. Bridget duly arrived and moved into the house.

She was wonderful and exactly what I needed. She took over the house, took on John and bossed both of us about. She changed our whole way of life forever in two weeks and when she left she suggested we put him in a home, saying to me "You don't need this dear, you're too young!"

After Bridget, we had a succession of other girls from this agency – all young South Africans with no training in caring, just a willingness to look after elderly people in return for board and lodging and pocket money to allow them to travel and visit other areas of the UK.

Towards the end of 2004, John was becoming very restless at night. His visits to the loo were more frequent and he was very disorientated and would try to go downstairs. I was getting very tired. Meanwhile, the carers were fast asleep in the basement, as Christie's rule was that they were entitled to 8 hours sleep at night and 2 hours off during the day!

Time to change the rules!

The Deighton Day Care Centre

In 2002, I discovered the Deighton Day Care Centre thanks to the Community Psychiatric Nurse. This was magic. He went there once a week to start with, and for many years it was a lifeline. In theory, there was a taxi service that would pick him up in the morning sometime between 8.00 and 9.00 and bring him back just as the children were coming out of school at 3:30.

In practice, that did not work, as first thing in the morning was never good for John, even in the old days when he was still John. Maybe that is why he became an actor because, unlike me, he improved as the day went on. I have always been a morning person.

So, three times a week I would drive him to the Deighton around 10.00 am and go shopping, visit a friend (whose husband also had dementia) on the way home, or just go home, collapse, cry and do the paper work, of which there was always plenty, before he came home at 3:30.

I never knew what he did at the Deighton, because he never talked about it. It was some time before I met lovely Bob. He taught pottery at the Deighton and took a wonderful photo of John and another patient working together. I had wondered what those weird objects were that sometimes came home with him, now known in the family as 'Dad's toast racks'. We were all astonished as he had never previously shown any interest in making anything, certainly not out of clay!

Sometimes he made things that vaguely resembled pots, which I gave away as Christmas presents with home grown scented geranium plants in them but they were few and far between.

Whatever he had done at the Deighton, and obviously he could never remember, he was often confused and muddled on his return. So, I would take him to the Cambridge Botanical Gardens to calm down, as it was at the bottom of our road.

Getting him past the children coming out of school was "interesting", but once inside the Gardens he was fine. He loved it there, and for some strange reason the people who worked there loved him too. We went nearly every day. Just that little walk through the glasshouses, to the café for a cup of tea and then to the fountains where he always sat on the same bench.

Gradually, the Deighton increased the number of days per week that they could have him from two to three and in 2006 they began to take him for two to four nights a month as well. Sometimes my step-father, Colin, would have appointments for his lung cancer at the Royal Free when John was in 'day care' at the Deighton. This required quite a feat of management. It meant persuading John that he needed to be up, showered, breakfasted and out of the house before 9:30 so that I could deposit him at the Deighton by 10:30 at the latest to be in London by 11.30 and at the Royal Free with Colin in a taxi by 12.00 ish.

Admittedly, Colin was never seen straight away and had to wait in a draughty corridor with a lot of other people, all similarly half-dressed. I can still see Colin in his hospital gown quietly reading his book or occasionally chatting to me, while a constant stream of people from all over the world walked past and went into various sick rooms as their names were called out. I had to listen out for his name as, like John, he was beginning to lose his hearing.

It was a very strange feeling being responsible for your step-father as well as your husband both of whom had become in different ways like small children.

The consultant thought Colin was wonderful. He would show the x-ray of his lungs and a scan to his students. Colin always said he did not understand x-rays to which the consultant would reply, "neither do my students." Then he would explain that the trouble with his lungs had not gone and asked if Colin would like some support from one of his staff to which the reply was always negative. Whereupon we would return to the dressing area. He would put his clothes back on and we would go back to the main hall, order a taxi and wait for it to arrive.

After lunch in their home in Queen's Grove, St John's Wood, I would get back in the car and drive to the Deighton, pick John up and go home.

This happened approximately once a month. Rarely did these appointments coincide with John's respites but Colin refused to go to the Royal Free with anyone else. He trusted me implicitly so I knew that if for any reason I could not go with him he would have been devastated and probably cancelled the appointment. Which is why, when in 2007 he asked me why he could not talk properly, kept losing his balance and falling in the house which resulted in his being admitted to hospital, I could not tell him because the consultant said that he was not to be told that the cancer had now moved into his brain. This feeling of guilt I shall carry to my grave.

With John, this was not a problem, as there was never anything wrong with him. It was the rest of us who were bonkers. We all have our own way of coping!

Looking back, I do not know how I juggled looking after John, trying to resolve the difficulties which arose from having carers in Queen's Grove to help look after Mummy and Colin's lung cancer appointments, but the Lord gives you strength to do what needs doing at the time.

The Deighton were wonderful. I would never have survived without them. By this time, John was very deaf and refusing to wear his hearing aids. Communication was very basic. He did not seem to understand anything, but responded to affection particularly from the grandchildren.

There came a point where even the Deighton could not cope with John. I began to find that they were giving him more and more medication during his respite times. These made him bolshy and difficult for me to deal with at home. It took me 3 weeks to wean him off them, by which time he was due to go back in again!

Thomasina kindly agreed to come with me to a review meeting, and I'm so glad she did! They explained that he no longer interacted with any of the activities, including the pottery he had previously loved. Indeed, despite the medication, it was still taking 3 members of staff to get him washed and dressed. They could not cope without the drugs; I could not cope if he took them, so we thanked them for their help, and took John home. He never went there again.

Memories of Dad

Thomasina

I looked after my dad once a month at the beginning to give my mother a break, which increased to fortnightly visits once he left the Deighton. At the time that he was getting bad, my daughter was 3 and my son was new born, so we would come over on the coach, as the children travelled free of charge, and it was easier to manage them if I was not also trying to negotiate the Friday night A14 traffic! Most of the trips passed without incident, but here are some more entertaining moments which may help to show what it was like.

The first time

The first time I remember coming to supply respite care, was when Mum was invited to spend a week in Tenerife with a friend, so I agreed to look after Dad for her. It was the first week in September, and Anna had just started nursery, so my husband said he would look after her, if I could take 6 week old Jeremy with me. At that stage, Dad was still able to read, just not to store the information for very long.

On that first day he asked me, "Where's your mother?" I tried "in Tenerife", and "in Spain" but despite begin well-travelled, he no longer had any idea where I meant. When I said "at the seaside", he became jealous, because he loved the sea! "Why didn't I go?" he asked. So I replied, "She's gone with her friend". "Oh, that dreadful woman!" came the reply, and he was no longer jealous!

This conversation was to be repeated several times over the course of the week, and I wrote the details down for him to read when I wasn't in the room, but it always ended positively – he was safe with me, and Mum was with "that dreadful woman!" The friend was supposed to have stopped for a cup of tea when she dropped my Mum home, which might have entailed her finding out she was known as "that dreadful woman!", but in the event she was running out of time, so our secret was safe!

He struggled equally to come to terms with Jeremy. I realized that whilst I had painstakingly explained to Anna that "Mummy has a baby in her tummy", all I'd told Dad was that I was pregnant, a phrase he clearly had not understood. So every day, several times a day, he would ask "What's that?" "It's a baby, Dad." To which he would reply either, "Typical of your mother to go off and leave us with one of those!" or "Doesn't do much, does it?"!

Most of the time it was easy looking after the two of them, as they both needed feeding at regular intervals, nappy changes and short, repeated entertainment. Both napped during the day and were up at various times in the night, and neither had a fixed routine, so I didn't need one either!

However, there was one morning when I realized I woke with a period. Blast! I'd forgotten all about those! I searched the house, but we'd used up Mum's stock – I'd have to go and buy something! The nearest shop was a 10 min walk. Both my charges were sound asleep, Dad upstairs and Jeremy in the carrycot in the dining room. What to do? If I woke the baby he would scream, take forever to get settled in the pram and probably wake Dad in the process. If I waited for them both to wake up, would Dad understand why he was being taken to a shop? The thought of explaining periods to an elderly man with dementia was too desperate for words, so instead I ran for it.

I have never run so fast in my life! I was there in 5 mins, grabbed what I needed, and ran for my life back, desperately hoping they hadn't managed to wake each other up and set the house on fire in my absence! I was certain every siren was going to my parents' house, and then coming to arrest me for neglect! Needless to say, the two of them had slept through the whole ordeal!

Saturday outings!

Most of our outings went fine. Endless toilet trips, endless food stops, and occasional opportunities to look around wherever we were in-between. This particular day we had gone to the local park. No-one was reliable at walking, so it was easier to drive and then everyone could choose how much they were willing to walk when we got there!

I parked the car, and unloaded the children, but my father refused to get out of the car. At 6'2" and 15 stone I couldn't force him, so I left him and took the children to play, returning every few minutes to the car park to check on him. This wasn't very satisfactory, so we tried bribing him with an ice cream! He liked the idea, but still refused to get out of the car! I brought it out to him, and then we all sat in the car eating our ice creams. He was still adamant he did not want to get out of the car, so I gave up and drove us all home.

As we pulled up outside the house he asked, "Where are we going? I thought we were going out!" and refused to get out of the car and walk in the house either! At least in the playground car park there was nowhere else to go, but outside the house he could get run over just getting out of the car, so we were all trapped! Then I had a brain wave! Mum had told us to have roast chicken for Sunday lunch, but a search of the fridge and freezer had drawn a blank – potatoes, veg but no chicken! Now was my chance – everyone was strapped in the car, refusing to get out – let's go buy a chicken!

I parked as close to the shop as I could, and gave 4-year-old Anna instructions. "Just make sure everyone stays in the car. Your brother and your grandfather both know how to undo their seatbelts – just don't let them get out. I'll be back as quickly as I can!" I ran into the shop, grabbed a chicken, rushed to the counter and was out as quickly as possible, but not quickly enough. There was my father walking purposely along the pavement, leaving a frantic child in the car. "I tried to stop him, Mummy, I did, but he was too strong. I tried to undo Jeremy but I couldn't get him out. I didn't know what to do! I'm sorry!" I sent her after her grandfather with instructions to grab his hand and help him cross any roads, but not try to change his direction as he was obviously a man with a mission!

I unstrapped Jeremy, shoved him in the pushchair and chased after them. In the event, Dad simply walked quickly and determinedly all the way home, with Anna running along behind. It was amazing how quickly he could go from totally bewildered, to desperate to go out, to totally focussed and equally desperate to go home! But, on the plus side, at least I now had a chicken for tomorrow's lunch, and they had all had their exercise for the day! And it wasn't far to run back and collect the car once they were all safely in bed!

The day he ran away.

We had all come to stay for our regular weekend visit, and some German friends had joined us on the Saturday. On the Sunday morning, Mum took Anna and the Germans to church, while I stayed at home with Dad and Jeremy (who was now 3) to get lunch ready.

With the chicken in the oven, I spent all morning trying to persuade my father to come to the Botanical Gardens for a walk, so he'd had an outing before everyone came home and he would be trapped for the afternoon. He refused to get out of his chair, so at 11:30 I'd given up and put the potatoes on while Dad and Jeremy watched TV in the upstairs living room.   Around 15mins later, Jeremy came downstairs.   "Where's your grandfather?" I asked. "He's gone out," came the innocent reply. "What do you mean, he's gone out?" I shouted. Mum and I always locked the front door after one of us went out to ensure that Dad couldn't leave unsupervised. Jeremy was most insistent, so I opened the front door, and, sure enough, there was my father almost at the end of the road!

In my panic I could only find one shoe, so I lurched up the road, shouting after him "Dad, Dad, stop!" I caught up with him on the corner, but he was most insistent that we had to cross the road to the Botanical Gardens. A couple saw me struggling with him, and offered to help. They were going to the gardens anyway, so I asked if they could just follow him and keep an eye.   Then I ran home again, grabbed my other shoe, explained what was happening to the family who were just returning from church.

Mum chased him back to the Gardens. He was sitting in the Gilmour building, waiting for his cup of coffee and refused to move until he had finished it. Luckily, nobody had started to eat until they returned.

Tessa

Taking my daughter Natalie to visit Mum and Dad was always difficult, because Dad didn't really understand who she was and would stare at her and pull her dress. This made her feel uncomfortable. It wasn't until I looked at the photo album that Mum had made for Dad that I realised why. Natalie looked exactly like one of Dad's sisters when she was her age.

After Deighton

Residential home

What to do next? I certainly couldn't cope with him at home 24/7. People used to say "Why don't you put him in a home dear? You've done it long enough." So I did.

We spent ages as a family, visiting the various places until we found one we liked. He spent one weekend in there, and then on the Monday morning they called me to come and take him home. Apparently, he threatened the staff, tried to jump out of the window and was generally so disruptive that they couldn't cope. He also had diarrhoea and sickness which they thought my daughter had brought in when she visited with the baby, and they were afraid it would spread to the other residents.

When I arrived, he was cowering in his underpants under the bed clothes covered in his own excrement and talking complete gibberish. To be fair, the manager was amazing with him and managed to get him out of bed, dressed and able to walk to the car. So, I took him home, cleaned him up, and rang the doctor. He didn't have an infection, and he gradually calmed down and life returned to normal. Amazingly enough, I didn't try residential care again!

Private trained carers

People often ask me how I got through the rest of John's life after the NHS wrote him off. The answer is I don't know. I remember falling on my knees in tears and saying, "Please Father help me. I have no idea what to do now." Thomasina went back to Coventry later that day and I was left feeling helpless and alone.

I remember washing up one day in 2005 and asking myself, if I won the lottery which I could not since I do not support it (it goes against my Christian beliefs), but if I did, what would I spend the money on? Sleep! This suddenly seemed the most precious commodity in life. Little things like that take on huge proportions when you are dealing with someone who is totally unpredictable.

So, I found a little, local care agency in Cambridge and discovered to my horror quite how expensive sleep was, especially at the weekend. Compromise was the answer. I would sleep in the newly converted basement four nights a week. The carer could sleep on a sofa bed in the sitting room with a brilliant device, provided by the occupational therapist, that was put under the mat outside the bedroom door and would let out a squeaky noise when John got up to go to the loo in the night, which he did frequently.

The secret was to walk behind him while he went down the stairs to the bathroom and then stand further down the stairs to prevent him from going down to the ground floor. That was fatal, as he would then sit in his chair and expect breakfast!!

This would also wake me up, as his chair was directly above my bed in the basement and then it would take the two of us the next hour or so to get him back to bed!

The carers were wondrous. They came at 9.00 pm and left at 6.00am four nights a week. At that time, it cost £10 an hour. But for us it was a life line. Even now, I hear people complaining that they only had four hours sleep. I think sleep is something we take for granted, but it is so important!

More importantly, they were all properly trained in how to deal with people with dementia, and wonderfully supportive of me. They would come for four hours at a time during the day, and stay overnight. Those carers were amazing! I still do not know how they did it.

Between them and my daughter Thomasina, who often came for the weekend from Coventry to give me respite, Friday night till Sunday afternoon, I kept my sanity for the last two years of his life.

Getting John to accept the carers was a different matter though. Mostly I got to the front door first, but I remember one day he opened the door to the lovely Denzel, and said, very politely, "Not today, thank you" before closing the door again! Then he turned to us and yelled "I won't have that terrible man in my house again!" I made John a coffee while Thomasina explained to Denzel that he couldn't come in today! Later, I phoned the agency and they found someone else to come for a few weeks until John had forgotten all about the issue and was happy to welcome Denzel again!

Supporting Mummy and Colin was now more by telephone than anything. I remember going with Colin that last time to the consultant at the Royal Free before he started to fall at home. He never understood why, and none of us were permitted to tell him.

Thank goodness it was never like that with John. He remained very mobile until he fell at my feet that day in May 2007.

Other people/places who made a difference

Neighbours

The people who were wonderful were people like Janet who came to my rescue when the carers were ill and John needed his prescription from the chemist. She used to ring every morning and say, "Hello popcorn, how are you? Sun's shining. Lovely day." But this particular morning I was distraught. The carer was ill herself and there was no replacement for her. Janet, who was losing her sight turned up in a taxi and said, "Where's the kettle? Where's the radio? Off you go popcorn. I'll be fine!"

I ran to the chemist and ran back half an hour later. John was still in bed. Janet was still smiling. So, all was right with my little world.

Sister Jane, one of the nuns who lived locally and taught Tessa and Cressie at the convent, Sophie, my neighbour and Jane, who worked for the Sisters, were all wonderful too. They would look after John so that I could go to the 8.00am service on a Sunday. Brian, who sometimes took the 8.00am service, would leave his car, come and have breakfast and go on to take the next service at St John's at 10:30 during the interregnum at St John's Church in Hills Road.

When my aunt who had looked after me in the USA during the war years died, I wanted to go to the funeral in Guildford. My friend and neighbour Fiona said she would look after John because her husband, who was a consultant at Addenbrooke's, would be out all day. This sounded perfect!

Unfortunately, the funeral was further away than I had realised, which meant returning home during rush hour! Fiona was wonderful. She guessed that I had been too optimistic about the timing for my return journey and had calmly made suitable arrangement for food. When I arrived back home two hours later than I had anticipated, Fiona was sitting quietly in the sitting room, knitting, whilst John was fast asleep in his favourite chair.

Other people tried to help, but it wasn't always successful. Thomasina's husband says he remembers coming to lunch for some family occasion. Apparently it was obvious that John recognized me, Thomasina and their children as important, even if he was no longer clear on their exact relationships. Other visitors he didn't recognize, and that clearly didn't bother him in the slightest! However, Simon says John spent the whole lunch looking at him and other family members with deep confusion, as if struggling to place them. It was so distressing to see, that Simon didn't come again.

The Alzheimer's Society

Joining them was the best thing I ever did. Barry Plumpton taught me everything I know and introduced me to a whole new lot of people who were in the same boat. We came from all walks of life and would probably never have met in ordinary life. However, looking after someone with any form of dementia is so different from anything else any of us have ever experienced because it is so unpredictable and there is no blueprint, as it is the person's personality that changes and we are all individuals.

Barry was wonderful. He was so patient and understanding. I remember the first time he came to the house and quietly handed me a piece of paper with his name and phone number on it. I remember saying, "I am fine. I don't need you. Go and help someone else." To which he replied very charmingly "I know you don't but you will, and when you do you will at least know what I look like" and with that he left the house.

I remember one day, I think it was in 2002, Barry Plumpton came to see me and I was getting frustrated not coping with John for whatever reason – nothing serious. Barry just looked at me and said very quietly, "Would you like to come with me to the Baker's Arms in Fulbourn? The Alzheimer's Society have lunch there once a month and everyone who is caring for someone is welcome. If you like, you can bring John with you."

Looking back, I still cannot believe that I casually said goodbye to John, got in the car and followed Barry to the pub. It was as though I did not care whether he was still there when I returned. So much for being a good wife and a responsible adult. One of the ladies there said, "I used to look like you when I was caring for Bert." I found myself thinking, "Where is Bert now?" but I didn't like to ask.

Barry said he will never forget my face as we drove there. That was the beginning of the most amazing relationship ever. Never before had I been with a group of people who were going through what I was going through. John was not a 'club' person.

Neither, I thought, was I. However, that lunch changed my life. I met all sorts of people from all walks of life, but the one thing we all had in common was that we were all carers. I had never thought of myself as a carer before, I was just John's wife.

In the marriage service, you say, "in sickness and in health," but I never thought for one minute that John would develop dementia. That was in my book far more likely to be me, since it was in my mother's family not his.

Later, after I had had something to eat and drink, it occurred to me that I had never left him on his own at home just like that and I began to feel guilty in case he had set fire to the house or even himself and quickly made an excuse and returned home, to find him fast asleep in his chair. It was fairly obvious he had not moved and had no recollections of my having left! Needless to say, I never did that again – but those lunches became a lifeline for me, once I had arranged someone to be with him while I was out. The best solution would have been to leave him at the Deighton in the morning and pick him up from there after lunch, but the timings of his stay at the Deighton rarely worked like that.

I did not fully appreciate the importance of these groups when Barry first invited me to them. Listening to other people's stories of how they coped and what they went through each day was both a humbling and informative experience for me. My life suddenly seemed easy compared to other people's. At least John was not violent, or if he was from time to time I knew it was only with me, and I knew how to stave off his anger before it erupted into violence. Other people were not so fortunate.

We lived together in our own house. Other people had to share their home with other members of the family.

Just meeting together on a monthly basis helped enormously. We took each other's advice. Being able to talk in a non-threatening environment was wonderful. We learnt so much from each other as everybody's coping mechanisms were different. Barry sometimes asked professionals to come to our meetings and apparently, they always left saying that they learnt more from us that we did from them.

Cambridge Botanical Gardens

John loved the Botanical Gardens. Luckily, unknown to me, the staff felt the same way about him! We used to go there nearly every day, sometimes twice in a day, especially towards the end of his life as he became very restless and would pace up and down at home picking things up and putting them down again anywhere so it was safer to take him out.

We always went the same way, taking the path to the glasshouses. He was fascinated by them, and really struggled when they were trying to do them up, so there were some doors that were closed to us. This he never understood. I often had to go and ask one of the staff to turn him around and let us go back the way we had come. The fact that the door was clearly marked closed never seemed to phase him.

We would then go on to the café, and then sit on his favourite bench. On a good day, he would sit there and fall asleep or pretend to count the fountains. From that seat, you can only see six of them.

Then we would walk back home across the grass. Sometimes, when it was busy, I would try to move him sooner as I never knew what he was going to do or say which could be embarrassing but most of the time he smiled sweetly at everyone, particularly the children. He loved children.

I thought the staff would have been thrilled when he died, but they said they could see what a lovely person he really was and how much we loved each other. Which is why, when he died, we had a little ceremony to dedicate a bench to him just outside the glass houses.

Wandlebury Woods

It is the beginning of May and once again I spent the morning at Wandlebury, sitting on the bench we provided in memory of our youngest daughter, Cressida. A stoat now lives in the copse we all helped to plant. In front of me, children were playing happily on the grass, laughing as they chased each other or were chased by their parents.

I hardly noticed through my tears, reading the lovely prayer that Anna had written in "Tidings" for those of us whose loved ones had died during that first week of May. Cressie loved nature. She always said that she preferred animals to people. "People let you down," she used to say. "Animals don't." How right she was!

I thought about her father and how few people understood what was wrong with him. He, too, loved Wandlebury and it was one of the few places I could take him where he felt comfortable and at ease away from the stares and disapproving looks that besieged him in the town.

Other memories

Night in K2

Everything becomes more complicated when someone has dementia. Here is what happened one night when we had to go to A and E.

Hospital appointments were always a nightmare. John never understood why he was there. He used to sit in A and E saying, "Why am I here? There is nothing wrong with me. What is the matter with you?" in a loud Shakespearian voice. He never lost his commanding presence and clarity of speech. I cringed and tried to change the subject, realising that I could not get away with publicly disowning him, although that was my natural instinct!

Anyway, this particular time, John had collapsed against a fence in Wandlebury Wood, after we had been to look at the copse we helped to plant in 1996 in memory of our youngest daughter. I drove him through to A and E at Addenbrooke's Hospital in Cambridge, where there is a big sign saying that everyone should have an ECG within 20 minutes of their arrival. Try two and a half hours later! By this

63

time, he was climbing the walls and being totally impossible. He had to be given Haloperidol to calm him down!

Eventually he was admitted onto the ward which is next to A and E. Everyone else was asleep. A young nurse from the Philippines pointed to a bed with a chair beside it. "Your chair, blanket," she said and disappeared. Somehow, I can't remember now, we persuaded John that he was to remove his shoes and lie on the bed. It was quite a performance. The next issue was that his bed was next door to the bathroom which was a 'wet room'. Brilliant. I decided every home should have one. Unfortunately, there was also a red emergency cord that John was desperate to pull!

I spent the next ten hours persuading him to stay in bed and stopping him from pulling the cord! I felt very sorry for the other occupants of the ward as nobody had any sleep that night!

In the morning, I was told that he had to wait to see the consultant. The poor little nurse had tried to give him some form of medication. I never discovered what it was for. Anyway, it did not matter as it was hurled at her by a now very frustrated and confused John.

The consultant eventually came onto the ward, and then proceeded to speak to all the other patients first, before finally turning to us. By this time John was being impossible even for me to control. The consultant looked at us and said, "How do you cope?" To which I replied, "I don't let him get like this!" Inside I was seething. I know that had he come to John first instead of last, we could have gone home!

Food

John loved his tummy! I often used food to get him to do something he did not want to do. For instance, if he had an appointment to go to the doctor in the morning, I could get him there by saying something like, "Eat your toast, and we will have coffee when we come back." He loved his mid-morning cup of coffee, and a biscuit which we quite often had at the Botanical Gardens.

Sometimes, on a good day, he would help with the cooking. This sounds odd but it was a bit like having help from my grandson Jeremy, who was two at the time. He would whisk the eggs for an omelette within an inch of their lives because once he had started, he had no idea when to stop!

Using a knife was lethal, which was hard because he loved cutting bread, but I was terrified he would cut himself as he lost all concept of danger to himself or anyone else. This apparently was perfectly normal as was putting the used crockery and cutlery in the fridge instead of the washing up machine!

Thomasina brought him a set of plastic dominoes from Tesco's. He loved them. We played dominoes by making wonderful patterns with them. One day the dominoes were on the table at breakfast time. I was upstairs making the bed when Anna, my five-year-old granddaughter called me down. "Quick Granny, Boppa's putting butter on one of the dominoes and I think he's going to eat it!" I rushed after her and sure enough he had covered the double blank in butter! It was clearly half way to his mouth!

Civilisation

John was a gent in the true sense of the word. To his dying day he would help me on with my coat, walk on the outside of me down the street which as the dementia progressed could be quiet terrifying at times as you can imagine. He never swore and was always polite. His grandmother said, "Born a gent where one wasn't needed." Little

Jonathan, Tessa's son and his grandson, is much the same!

As you get older, life gains a different perspective. Memories fade and matters you thought you knew, somehow are not there anymore but the important things remain. Love being the chief one. If you really love someone you can overcome all the little incidents of life however hard it may seem at the time. John was never deliberately unkind to anyone. Yes, he said things he shouldn't and did things he shouldn't, but it was not on purpose. His mind could no longer reason clearly and he lost control over his bodily functions and made me realise how thin the outward layer of civilisation is. We spend years training our minds and bodies to do things in certain ways that are acceptable, but dementia, in all its forms, removes that fragile form of civilisation which was called 'acceptable behaviour' and we become more like animals.

Hygiene

This was a huge problem and quite probably the reason why he had so many urine infections. Sometime in 2006 John either could not or would not climb into the bath to stand under the shower. This was so unlike him. He loved his shower!

Trying to keep him clean became a nightmare all of its own.

The Deighton were wonderful with him. I often took him there in tears because I had unsuccessfully tried to clean him up before he went. They never complained. "Never mind dear. Just leave him with us. We'll deal with it. Off you go." was the attitude. I really admired them and often asked how they did it. to which they would reply cheerfully "We go home at night and switch off." I longed to do that myself!!

The NHS provided 20 pads a month. These were woefully inadequate. One morning, I went to A and E in Addenbrooke's, walked into one of the clinics and asked one of the nurses if I could have a pack of pads for John and one for Helen next door – having first explained my predicament – and much to my astonishment they said, "Of course you can" and went to find them! Needless to say, I never did it again.

Accusations

One evening, a man rang up and accused John of molesting his 14-year-old daughter. When I remonstrated with him, he replied, "You do not know what he gets up to after 10:30 at night. To which I replied, "Yes I do. He is upstairs in bed fast asleep. The front door is locked and he does not know how to open it." All these years later I am still reeling from shock that anyone would think something like that of John. How strange people are. Who was this man? Where did he get that idea from? And how did he get our phone number, unless he looked it up in the book?

Coping strategies

The real problem with dementia whatever its cause is that there is not a blueprint for survival on any level. You literally have to go with the flow which is why attending a group meeting composed of like-minded people is so important for our sanity as much as anything.

It really is essential to leave the house and do something 'just for you' as often as you can, even if it is only going for a walk. I got to the stage when leaving the house to go down the road to the chemist on my own was exciting. How sad is that?!

St John's Church in Hills Road was a lifeline. They used to have a service at 8.00am on a Sunday morning and various people would come and be in the house for an hour so that I could go. It was wonderful. Yes, the congregation was rarely more than four, so I do see that it was probably not the best use of church facilities, but it meant a lot to me.

John was not difficult or nasty on purpose. It was just relentless, like a dripping tap only, unlike a dripping tap, there was no solution to the problem. Often, I found that just quietly getting up from my chair, leaving the room, counting to ten and then coming back in helped settle my thoughts for a little while.

I keep being told that I am so knowledgeable on the subject, which is why I have written here about my own experiences. However, because we are all different, this will not benefit everyone. Patience, understanding and faith in the Lord above is what kept me going all the time. However, I have to admit that part of me was relieved when he died because I was exhausted – no other reason. Now I miss him.

However, situations arise now and I flounder but the John I married would have resolved them in a jiffy! He would simply have laughed and said in his inimitable Yorkshire accent, "You are looking at it backwards way round," and then we would both have laughed.

Laughter is a great healer as you all know. John always had a wicked sense of humour which he never lost totally. Mine on the other hand was not nearly so predictable. He taught me to see the funny side of things in a way that no-one else did. Am I losing it as I get older, or is it just that the world has become more serious? All I know is that I do not laugh as often as I used to.

Tears flow more often than laughter. The world has become such a cruel place. Or is it just that the technological age has made us more aware? It was only just beginning when John was nearing the end of his life and I was so involved in his care that I did not have time to take it in and I have never really come to terms with it even now, seven years later. My second daughter, Tessa, tries so hard to help, but my failing eyesight is always my excuse. She has been a 'star' since her father died.

Now I am on the committee of a local Rethink group and am astonished at the situations the carers tell of their lives. Most of us feel isolated. Often just to go for a walk helps diffuse a difficult situation and gives you a chance to recharge your batteries. For me it was the Botanic Gardens, but I was lucky enough to live within easy walking distance of them.

John's death

John hardly slept at all the night before. He kept wandering around the house. Up and down the stairs, in and out of bed. I followed him, worried that he would fall and hurt himself.

Finally, he walked into the sitting room, let out a loud scream and fell beside the grand piano. I was worried that he had hurt himself but he had not. He lay on the floor twitching violently. When I watched him topple I dialled 999. It was 7.00am.

Suddenly, he stopped twitching and lay quite still. I thought he was dead. The ambulance people took a long time to appear, so I rang Tony, the retired doctor who lived next door, and he came around in his dressing gown at the same time as the ambulance men. I was still in my nightie. I thought John was dead, but he wasn't.

The ambulance men were wonderful. They somehow managed to move John onto a sort of shiny mattress and moved him down the stairs while I got dressed. We left Tony waving from his front door step and set off. Poor Tony, unknown to us, had left without a key and stood there for hours until his wife Helen was finally able to make her way downstairs to let him in!

Thank goodness Thomasina was with me when the phone rang at 7.00am the following morning, saying that he had gone. I can still hear the shaky voice of the nurse saying that she had done all she could to revive him, but he had not been seen by another doctor after he left A and E. She was very upset about this, but I was not. I had already said my goodbyes to him before I left on the Friday. I knew instinctively he would have died with or without any member of the medical profession being there.

The downside from the family's point of view was trying to arrange the funeral, because hospital protocol says that two doctors have to have seen the patient in the last two weeks in order to sign the death certificate. How they got around that we shall never know, but it did give everyone a chance to come if they wanted to.

Putting my mother in a home

Since John died 10 days after Colin, I suddenly found myself responsible for the welfare of my mother. As nobody was allowed to tell Colin what was wrong with him, he had planned his will assuming wrongly that Mummy would die before him. But God had other ideas.

My sister and step-sister took it in turns to ring me and ask what I was going to do about Mummy. Brookside was not an option. So, I set about trying to find somewhere else for her to go. She clearly could no longer live in Queen's Grove.

I combed through the various options very slowly as my brain was not really functioning properly and remembered that one home I had visited as a possible for John should life in Brookside become too difficult was Hilton Park in Bottisham.

It had once been a Rectory and was set in lovely grounds between Cambridge and Newmarket. It was more expensive than the other places I had seen, but Colin was not short of a penny or two, so I rang them and they agreed to take her and within minutes, so it seemed, the whole thing was arranged including transport from Queen's Grove to Hilton Park and I arrived on the door step shortly after Mummy did!

Little did I know that this was to become her home for the next three years. It was a big success. They loved her. She was no trouble, being completely immobile. Everything had to be done for her by two carers. I visited her two or three times a week.

The girls and their children came frequently as well. When the sun shone we pushed Mummy in her wheelchair out into the lovely garden and her own room on the ground floor looked over the garden so she could watch the squirrels playing from her bed.

I arranged for her to have physiotherapy twice a week and she also had aromatherapy. She looked well and seemed happy. It was very strange for me going to visit my mother in a home. I do not know if she even knew who I was. She smiled a lot and no longer suffered from urine infections or needed enemas as she had at home, and seemed happy and contented.

I still feel guilty about not looking after her myself. My sensible, practical side says that was ridiculous, as Brookside was not built for people in wheelchairs, but my emotional side says that daughters are supposed to look after their mothers when they can no longer fend for themselves, aren't they?

Logic did not really come into it. After all, Mummy had never looked after us. Nanny did. She was "on the telly," known to the public as Mary Malcolm, and only came to be with us if Nanny was on holiday. If I am honest, I never really knew her when I was growing up. Now would be the time for us to get to know one another. However, by the time Colin was dead and Mummy was in Hilton Park it was all too late. She had lost her power of speech and anyway, too much water had flowed under the bridge.

Mummy developed a chest infection at the beginning of October which did not respond to antibiotics. The doctor for the home was wonderful. She and I stood together at the bottom of Mummy's bed watching her inbound breathing and decided between us that she would be better off just being made comfortable where she was, rather than moving her into hospital.

I spent the last week of her life summoning all the family and encouraging them to visit when possible and basically sitting by her bedside until she died.

Annabel, my sister, was home from New York anyway to go to something in Paris. I persuaded her to come to Hilton Park first and then she came back after Paris and we sat together until Mummy died.

Annabel's husband, Anthony, came on his own and we stayed in Brookside, planning the funeral. They went back to New York and I went to Nepal. All very strange. Looking back on it now six years later, I ask myself, "How did you do it?" and the answer comes back loud and clear, "If God wants you to do something, He gives you the strength." Admittedly, I only just managed the trekking in Nepal to raise money for the Alzheimer's Society, but it is the most beautiful country and they are such lovely people, I strongly believe that if a chance comes up to visit – Go for It!

Dealing with the aftermath

Even now I find relationships hard. Life moved on while I was looking after John. The technological age took off and left me behind. I feel I do not belong in this world anymore. People talk about things that I do not begin to understand and I can see them there staring at me obviously thinking, "Which planet does she live on?"

After John died, people would come up to me in the street and enquire after my health before telling me how wonderful I was the way I looked after John. I wasn't wonderful. I used to cry and moan a lot. Anyway, how did they know? They never came near us.

It is very hard to be with people who have never been in this situation. I have forgotten how to talk, show emotion, laugh, stupid things that other people take for granted. I suppose I was used to things changing every five minutes, seconds sometimes that 'in-depth' feelings, ideas, etc. just did not happen. Life moves on. You cannot stay stuck in the past, but it is hard. Lovely Tony from next door has died, so has my cleaner Veronica's husband John.

Faith

We are all different and come from different perspectives, different ideas, different parts of our social structures and different attitudes to faith, which for me is the central point. If I did not have faith in the Lord above, I would have gone under years ago when our youngest daughter died.

Faith means different things to different people according to their culture. I admire the people who believe that this is it. There isn't anything else. I personally could not live on that basis. What would be the point? But, as I have already said, we are all different.

John always said that he did not believe in anything. But when Cressie died, he read that chapter from St Paul's letter to the Corinthians so beautifully that it moved the congregation to tears and people talked about it for years later. So, as I say, you never know. My own faith deepens with age, as does my admiration for people who are willing to go that extra mile in coping and coming to terms with losing someone you knew and loved to that cruel disease called dementia in all its forms.

I often hear people say, "How do you cope on your own? How did you cope with John all those years?" and the answer is quite obvious. I did not and I do not now. It is my faith that keeps me going. I keep telling myself that he never gives you more than you can bear whatever your circumstances. This is not easy and I often feel like saying yes, but he has gone too far this time. Then suddenly the sun will come out either literally or metaphorically and all will be well again.

We are here for such a short time. How will we be remembered? I have moaned a lot about my lot in life. Why? We are all given different gifts. How we use them is up to us. Often it seems that my role is more of an observer than a carer. But like St Paul says in Philippians, I have learnt to be content with whatever life throws at me. He put it much better than I can.

I want to say, "Why me?" But you can't ask questions like that. When life is hard and the future seems bleak, that is when our Christian faith comes to the fore and we remember that He never gives us more than we can bear. I used to say that often to myself when John was literally driving me crazy, followed by He is really pushing it this time, and then John would say something or give me one of his huge smiles and the sun would come out on my life and sanity was restored. It probably sounds silly, but I have learnt to appreciate the little things in life and to be grateful for the beauty of the sunrise over the Botanical Gardens and this gives me strength to face another day.

What next?

Attitudes to Dementia

Life has moved on since 2007 but the stigma is still there. You still see the pitying looks in people's eyes when they see you are caring for someone with dementia before they hurry on to concentrate on their own lives.

I suppose it is because dementia is so unpredictable and there are still no solutions to the ever-growing problem. At least it is talked about which is a step in the right direction.

A friend rang me after John died asking if he ever got over that 'funny dementia thing'.

I love it when people talk about diet and exercise, both mental and physical, as being the key to prevention. If only it were that simple!

Care, Costs and Research Funding

When John was first diagnosed, I remember being told by someone from the Alzheimer's Society that it was a very expensive illness. This I thought at the time was a strange thing to say, but quickly realised how right she was.

Placing a relative with dementia is care is a) very expensive and b) far from ideal as you have no control over the treatment of your loved one. Very few people feel they have done the right thing by doing this. A lot, like me, feel that they had to as there was not another option but it is still far from satisfactory.

Most people struggle through on their own and eventually give up. The days of keeping the care within the family are gone because we all lead such diverse lives often not within easy reach of each other.

When we put our loved ones in a home, this is rarely satisfactory for anybody and should only be used as a last resort, as someone suffering from dementia needs to be in familiar surroundings with familiar people looking after them for as long as possible.

I was fortunate, as was my step-father. We could afford help. Most people cannot. The NHS is so strapped for cash that you really have to be virtually bankrupt before they will step in and take the person with dementia into full time care.

I realise how lucky I was that for me John died at home when he had that fatal convulsion at the beginning of May 2007. Yes, the paramedics came and took him into hospital but he was mostly asleep and had no idea he was there.

Yes, Dementia is more talked about than before. But there is very little funding or help on offer. It is hard to cope on your own.

I am hoping and praying that over seven years later, it is being talked about more. There is still very little money going into research and it does not have the same appeal as other diseases. But, as we are an ageing population, more and more of us are going to die from some form of dementia, so it does need to be taken seriously.

Moving on

We are all here on a journey just some of us are more aware of this than others. It has taken me many years to understand fully that the Lord never gives us more than we can bear and that he has a purpose for each one of us only we do not always understand what that purpose is. If you had ever told me what I would have done in my 70s, I would never have believed them, but here I am still in Cambridge in a little house with a little courtyard garden designed by my 9-year-old granddaughter, Tessa's daughter, Natalie.

In 2014, I joined a U3A walking group. It is a very strange feeling going for a walk with a group of people who, for the most part, are about 10 years my junior just for the sake of going for a walk. We are not raising money for anything or anyone. It seems very strange to me. The idea is a good one. We meet once a week in a pub car park at 9:30am, go in, order something simple for lunch and then return approximately three hours later, having walked about six miles. Some of the walkers are used to going for long walks. Most of us are townies who rarely walk anywhere. We are from all walks of life.

New life is here in my youngest grandson Jonathan – in many ways the replica of his grandfather. There are flowers out, birds are building nests. Life goes on. You cannot stop it. It does not help to dwell in the past, but that is easier said than done!

Now six years later, through the Dementia Care Support Service run by the NHS, I am helping other people who are trying to come to terms with caring for someone with dementia.

I remember towards the end of John's life I used to lie in my bed crying, "Please Lord, just take him." I was exhausted and could not do this any more. Then, when he died, I felt guilty, partly because I hadn't expected to survive myself. Yet here I am, seven years later, writing about it – still not quite sure why I am still here – but if these few words that I have written will help somebody else who is suffering in the way that I did, then I can be happy.

Jemima Atkinson

About the Author

The threat of Alzheimer's has been a constant in Jemima Atkinson's life. On her mother's side it struck great grandmother, grandmother and mother. Jemima always thought "it's my turn next"

Jemima's childhood was shaped by being sent to America when aged two, to escape the war. After three years in California, she sailed to Portugal on the Serpa Pinto, which famously transported more than 110,000 passengers, many refugees, during the hazardous war years. Jemima stayed with Quakers for four days in Lisbon, before taking the hazardous flight back to war torn England.

She did not have anywhere to live and as a five year old found herself living in in bits of other people's lives. Her parents were too immersed in their own careers, working for the BBC in wartime, not living with their children or even each other. Her mother worked as an Announcer and her father was in charge of the Script Department. Thus her nanny and grandparents featured largely in Jemima's childhood.

As a result, Jemima felt the importance of bringing up children so that they knew their parents. Wanting to work with children, she trained at St George's, a teaching hospital in Tooting, London and then went on to work at the then Chelsea Children's Hospital, qualifying as a Paediatric Nurse.

Supporting children evolved into a journalistic career, with the children's magazine 'Princess'. She met the debonair actor John Atkinson at a friend's party and marriage and children soon followed. In the 1974 the family moved out of London to Hertfordshire and then to Cambridge for the children's education.

Faith and the local church were also very important to Jemima and she took an active role in teaching in the Sunday School.

Always the thought of Alzheimer's and "my turn next" was in the back of her mind, till fate cruelly intervened. It was not Jemima who developed Alzheimer's, it was John. The experience of caring for him led to her telling this story.

Jemima is now involved with research for the Alzheimer's Society. Her official title is 'Research Network Volunteer'. Apparently, constructive criticism from people like Jemima is much appreciated by PhD students!

Jemima is donating the proceeds of this book of her experiences to Alzheimer's charities and research.